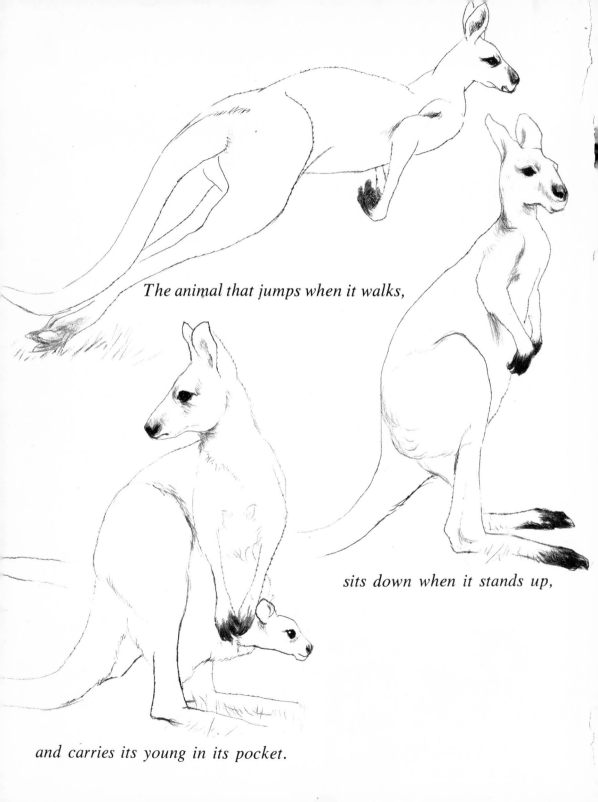

The animal that jumps when it walks,

sits down when it stands up,

and carries its young in its pocket.

YOUNG KANGAROO

By Margaret Wise Brown

Illustrated by Symeon Shimin

New York: William R. Scott, Inc., Publisher

Library of Congress Catalog Number 55-5097

COPYRIGHT MCMLV BY WILLIAM R. SCOTT, INC. MADE IN U.S.A.

It was a little kangaroo—how little you would never believe. It was one inch long when it was born —the size of a baby mouse, the size of a child's toe, the size of a baby kangaroo.

Then, blind and naked and helpless as it was, it began climbing arm over arm through the fur on its mother's stomach up towards the pouch that was to be its own dark nursery for the first five or six months of its life.

It took thirty minutes to make that first journey, arm over arm from hair to hair through a soft woolly forest of fur. At one point the baby kangaroo got caught in the fur. His feet were all tangled in hairs and he could not go on. The mother kangaroo leaned slowly down and nudged him on his way. Then he started crawling again, and in time he got there, safe in the mother kangaroo's pouch.

Deep in the pocket of the pouch, the baby kangaroo found his mother's breast, and he hung on for dear life. For the next few months, that was all he had to do. Later on, he would grow a little fur coat of his own, he would have a little kangaroo shape of his own, and when the time came he would come peeking out at the world about him.

But that time was still to come, and in the mean-
time his mother went hopping about over the grassy
plains of Australia. And to see her bounding along,
clearing high bushes and fences with her long kangaroo tail streaming out behind her, no one would
ever have suspected that in her pouch she harbored
a little growing kangaroo.

But the little fellow in her pouch knew that he was there. And all this time he was growing and growing, bigger and bigger. The first month he grew as big as a baby squirrel, the next month he was the size of a puppy dog. And when he was about as big as a small monkey, in the fourth month, he came peeking out.

He got tired of riding around in the dark. Where was he going? Why was everything still and quiet some of the time, while at other times everything was moving?

He couldn't see yet, but slowly and cautiously he stuck his little nose out and sniffed the air. And, as he sniffed, he found that the air changed. The more he sniffed, the more it changed. Sometimes it was cold and damp, sometimes it was sweet and dry, sometimes it was just empty of smell like space. Sometimes he smelled other kangaroos. They smelled like big warm strangers. Sometimes he smelled sweet acacia and spicy eucalyptus trees, sometimes the prickly dry smell after rain.

no eyes
next page ?
P. 14

12

no eyes!

It was all very curious—because it was always changing. The little kangaroo began to suspect that there was something in the world beyond his own nose that he ought to find out about.

And so one day, he followed his nose, and his eyes peeked out. His newly-opened eyes were blinded by a blaze of light. He popped his head back into the pouch, back into the familiar darkness that didn't hurt his eyes. But that first blaze of light had been exciting to him, as it is to all young animals who first open their eyes. And the little 'roo popped his head out again and again.

Once when he popped his head out, it was dark—
not as dark as his mother's pouch, but there was no
white blaze of light to blind his eyes. He looked up
and saw little far-off pricks of light above him. The
stars were far away, but they didn't blind his eyes like
the blaze of daylight. They were little lights that he
could look at.

The little 'roo knew through his eyes what his nose
had first told him. The world was full of changes—
changing smells and changing lights. What was behind the changes he would some day find out.

Fast as his hair and teeth and bones grew, his
curiosity grew faster. Soon his eyes began to focus.

16

Tall blurs went by him as his mother leaped along, little blurs went by him, and blurs that smelled like other kangaroos leaped about him. And gradually in all this blur he saw trees and bushes and the other kangaroos, and the blurs became living and growing things. The baby kangaroo could see.

From the time the little kangaroo could see all the trees, bushes, the far horizons, and the other kangaroos—from the time he could begin to see what it was that he smelled—the little kangaroo was busy every seeing minute of the day. But most of the time he was very busy sleeping and eating and just growing, for it takes a lot of sleeping and eating and peering about and wondering to make any little animal grow—a child, a kitten, or a kangaroo.

19

And then, one day when his mother took flying leaps over green bushes that brushed past the baby 'roo's face, he reached out his little paw and grabbed a green leaf. He put it in his mouth, and left it there and played with it. He liked it so much, he swallowed it. From then on the little 'roo was nibbling at everything his quick little paws could grab.

There were five ways of finding out what something was, the little 'roo learned. You could smell what it smelled like. You could see what it looked like. You could feel what it felt like. You could hear what it sounded like. Most things, the little 'roo discovered, were quiet, and, anyway, he was more interested in putting things in his mouth and tasting what they tasted like.

If he liked what something tasted like and if it was good for him, he felt good. If it wasn't good for him, he felt bad—he felt bad in his stomach. The things that made him feel good he grew to know by their smell and by the look of them, and he grabbed them as often as he could see them and reach out for them —green buds and tender little leaves and soft thorns.

20

And then one day he reached out so far to grab at some bright green grass blades that he pulled himself right out of the pouch. And there he was, tumbling on the ground, apart from his mother. He didn't stay that way long! He was frightened to death. And, quick as the flight of an Australian bird, certain as a streak of lightning, he scrambled back and dove head first into his mother's pouch, and he didn't come peeking out of it again until the next day.

But the next day, much to his surprise, the first thing he did was to grab at a tuft of green, and out he came again on the ground, and back he dove into the pouch.

Before long he had pulled himself out again, and this time he stayed a little longer and looked about him. He was standing in the grass on the world. He was standing on his own two feet. He nibbled at the grass and it tasted good. He listened carefully and he heard the wind in the grass. He could hear the wind, but he couldn't taste it or see it. He saw a black bug with shiny wings.

This was the world of Australia. Great plains of waving green grass grew all about him. As far as you could look there was distance, and about him, where the little 'roo could see them, were other kangaroos— great warm woolly animals, propped against their tails and twitching their noses.

When the little 'roo had been on the ground often enough to feel at home there, he sat up and leaned back against his tail and twitched has nose just like any other kangaroo, and his loose gentle paws hung down like the idle paws of a bunny.

27

At this age the little 'roo was not any bigger than a
beaver. He was smaller than the bushes. He had to
stretch his baby neck way up to get at the tender top
leaves of the bushes. His mother never helped him.
She knew that the longer he stretched, the stronger
he would grow.

28

Traveling around with his mother was like flying. She took great bounds that cleared the earth and sent her through the air, high above fences and bushes. She could easily have jumped right over a horse or a man if she had met one.

One day she did meet a man—a man with a gun. She got so excited she ran towards him instead of away from him, and jumped right over him. He was so surprised he fell flat on his face, and his gun went off, low along the ground.

But out on the plains the kangaroos seldom met other animals. There were no meat-eating animals on the whole continent of Australia except wild dogs. All the other animals lived on grass, so that wild dogs and men were the only enemies of the bounding kangaroo.

The kangaroo, though he could not bite, could kick the daylights out of his enemies with his powerful hind foot or rip them open with the long razor-like claw of his third hind toe. He seldom used his little limp forepaws, but he could use them, too, if he wanted to.

30

One day he was bounding along inside his mother's pouch when he heard her heart begin to beat faster. His own little heart began to beat faster. He peeked out of the pouch, and then he heard barking and baying. The grasses and the bushes and the trees were all rushing by beneath him as his mother leaped along. She seemed to be flying over everything, as she went tearing along. And the long sound of the hounds grew louder and nearer in his ears.

31

His mother's heart began to thump wildy, and then
to thud. Suddenly, as they sailed over a clump of
bushes, she reached down with her front paws and
threw him into a bush. Before he could prop himself
up and look around, she had gone and he was alone—
alone in the middle of a bush.

A great snuffing and padding of paws went past
him. It was the wild dogs that were chasing his
mother, but he didn't know that. He didn't know that
his weight in his mother's pouch had slowed her
down, so that, if she had not thrown him off into a
bush, she would have been caught by the dogs and
both would have been killed. But, by throwing him
into a bush, she saved him and she saved herself.

Only how would a little kangaroo know that? All
he knew was that his mother wasn't there. For the
first time in his life he was alone. Alone in a bush.
Silence fell about him after the dogs had passed and
he was alone in the world.

34

Alone. It was awful, when you had never been
alone before. It was like the sound behind the wind.
At first the little kangaroo couldn't stand it, and he
fought to get out of the bush. He whimpered and he
wailed. But then he got more used to it and grew tired
in his grief. After a while he whimpered himself into
a cold little sleep.

His mother, with no little kangaroo in her pouch to weigh her down, easily got away from the dogs. Then she returned to look for her tossed-out baby. But when she got there, it was dark, and she could not see him. There were so many bushes. The air was cold and dry, and, sniff as she sniffed, she couldn't smell him. By that time he had cried himself to sleep, so she couldn't hear him. But she knew he was some-where nearby, and so she waited there all night for some sign from him.

Late that night the little kangaroo woke up. Stars were cold above him. The wind was cold, and the branches of the bush were cold. He remembered—he was all alone. He whimpered a thin little whimper.

41

And then, not far off, he heard a familiar snuffle, and his mother came leaping up to him. She lifted him up in her forepaws and put him back head first into her pouch, where he was dark and safe and warm.

42

Back in the pouch the little kangaroo closed his eyes. Near him his mother's heart was beating slowly —thump, thump, thump. He was home. He was with his mother, and his little wild heartbeats came more slowly. Behind closed eyes, sleep came to him again— only this time a long warm sleep, full of tender grasses and little kangaroo dreams. 139